Black History

Author   Walter A. Hazen
Illustrator   Margo Burian

**SCHOOL OF EDUCATION
CURRICULUM LABORATORY
UM-DEARBORN**

Reproducible for classroom use only.
Not for use by an entire school or school system.

EP351 © Highsmith LLC 2007
4810 Forest Run Road
Madison, WI 53704

Table of Contents

The Hands-on Heritage series has been designed to help you bring culture to life in your classroom! Look for the "For the Teacher" headings to find information to help you prepare for activities. Simply block out these sections when reproducing pages for student use.

Great African Kingdoms

Were European traders ever surprised when they first touched land on the west coast of Africa in the fifteenth century! To them, Africa was the "Dark Continent," a region inhabited by backward and savage people. Most believed ridiculous stories that circulated at the time. One of the most ridiculous was the belief that Africans had no heads—that their eyes and mouth were located in their chests!

West Africa was not backward at all. A number of mighty kingdoms had arisen there. These kingdoms were rich in culture. Their artists and craftsmen were very skilled at making such items as sculptures and masks. Masks were used in many ceremonies. Some had religious significance; others were designed for hunting and other rites and celebrations.

Project

Make an African mask. Pretend it is a hunting mask, designed to frighten and to give the wearer power over animals.

Materials

- cardboard box
- tempera paint
- glue
- string
- pen
- scissors
- hole punch

Directions

1. Draw the outline of your mask on part of a cardboard box. Make it the correct size to fit your head. Cut it out.

2. Cut out holes for eyes.

3. Use part of the box scraps to cut out a nose and mouth. Glue these to your mask.

4. Paint your mask a bright color. Paint the nose and mouth a different color. Include other markings that you think would make your mask more frightening.

5. Punch a hole in each side of your mask. Insert a piece of string to hold it to your face.

Extension Activity

Many African Americans today are proud of their African heritage. Using an encyclopedia or some other source, look up and make a list of some of the early African kingdoms that existed on the African continent at the beginning of the Age of Exploration.

Middle Passage

A dark period of American history began in the year 1619. That is when a Dutch ship landed in Jamestown with 20 Africans aboard. Although these unfortunate souls were sold as indentured servants and not slaves, that year is usually regarded as the beginning of the slave trade in America.

The ordeal slaves had to endure on a slave ship across the Atlantic almost defies description. The two-month journey was referred to as the "middle passage." First, Africans were rounded up and kept in fort-like stockades along the coast of west Africa. Many of these future slaves had been captured by other African tribes and sold to white slave traders. When a slave ship arrived at a fort, Africans were crammed together in the hold of the vessel for the long voyage to America.

Can you picture how miserable such a journey might have been? People were forced to lie prone in a space often no more than 18 inches high. They were chained together, having to lie in their own waste and vomit. Some could not eat because of the stench. Disease was rampant, and many died along the way. Others went insane. Still others killed the person next to them to have more room. When someone died, his or her body was unchained and thrown overboard. Slave traders were not bothered by some of their valuable cargo dying before reaching the New World. Their profits were so high that a few deaths along the way mattered little.

Project
Create a dialogue (conversation) with a friend about the Middle Passage.

Materials
- research materials
- pen or pencil
- notebook paper

Directions
1. Read more about slave ships and the Middle Passage in an encyclopedia or on the Internet.
2. Pretend you are an ex-slave who came to America on a slave ship and that you were later freed by a kind master.
3. Create a conversation you might have had with a friend in which you describe what conditions were like on a slave ship.

Extension Activity
The slave trade in North America began in the 1600s and continued into the nineteenth century. While slaves in some northern states were eventually granted their freedom, slavery continued in the South until after the Civil War. Why do you think northern slave holders freed their slaves, while it took a war to end slavery in the South? Write your thoughts in several paragraphs.

Crispus Attucks

Crispus Attucks is often referred to as the first American to die in defense of his country. He was the first black American to die in the struggle for freedom against Great Britain.

On March 5, 1770, an angry mob of colonists confronted a group of British sentries in front of the Customs House in Boston, Massachusetts. Crispus Attucks, a former slave, was at the front of the crowd. He and the others shouted insults at the sentries and began to pelt them with rocks, snowballs, and clubs. The sentries called for help. Soon other British soldiers and their officer appeared on the scene. "Bloody Backs! Lobster Scoundrels! Rascals!" shouted Attucks and the others. Fearing for their lives, the soldiers fired into the mob, killing five. History refers to the incident as the Boston Massacre.

Regardless of which side was at fault, Crispus Attucks and the other victims were hailed as heroes by many colonists.

Project
Draw a cartoon in four panels.

Materials
- sheet of white paper
- pencil
- crayons or colored pencils

Directions
1. Draw a cartoon in four panels illustrating the Boston Massacre.
2. Use "word bubbles" to show what people in the cartoon are saying.
3. Color your cartoon panels.

Extension Activity
Why do you think British soldiers were often called "Lobster Scoundrels" and "Bloody Backs"? Check an encyclopedia or American history book to find out.

York

In 1804, Meriwether Lewis and William Clark set out on a journey to explore a vast amount of land recently purchased from France. That land was called the Louisiana Territory, and it included most of what is now the central part of the United States.

Among the crew that accompanied Lewis and Clark was Clark's personal slave, a large black man named York. York proved to be a valuable asset to the expedition. The Native Americans that the party met along the way were in awe of the man. Because of his presence, relations with the various tribes were generally good.

It is believed that York knew how to keep the Indians entertained. He reportedly danced and told wild stories. According to legend, he sometimes played the role of a crazy man, telling the Indians that he once was a wild man who ate people.

His antics and story telling, however, did not win York a place in American history. What did was the fact that he was the first black person to cross America all the way to the Pacific Ocean.

Project
Make a journal entry and drawing about York. (Both Lewis and Clark kept a journal or notebook of their expedition. They recorded events and made sketches of things they saw.)

Materials
- paper and pencil
- crayons or colored pencils

Directions
1. Pretend you are either Lewis or Clark on their famous expedition.

2. Make an entry describing something York did on a particular day. You can have him playing the fiddle or dancing, or you can write about how he interacted with Native Americans.

3. In the margin of your journal entry, draw and color a small picture illustrating York's actions.

Extension Activity
Create a dialogue that might have taken place among several Native Americans when they first encountered York.

Plantation Life

Life on a plantation was extremely difficult for African slaves. They worked in the fields from before dawn until after dark. Often they were beaten and humiliated by cruel overseers (bosses). They had no hope of ever becoming free, as they and their children were doomed to a lifetime of slavery.

Plantation slaves, however, were occasionally allowed moments of rest. On Sundays they could gather for such activities as games and dances. Many chose to attend church. Or, they could make one of their favorite dishes: okra soup. This was made by boiling fresh okra with other ingredients. A typical recipe is provided below.

Project
With the help of an adult, cook a pot of okra soup.

Materials
- 1 cup of peeled and chopped tomatoes (or, 2 cans of diced tomatoes)
- 2 cups of sliced or canned okra
- 1 cup of cooked corn
- 2 cups of water (or chicken or beef broth)
- salt, black pepper, and ground red pepper (don't overdo it)
- 1 slice of bacon (optional)

Directions
1. Place contents in a large pot. Bring to a boil.
2. Reduce heat to low. Cover and simmer for about 15 minutes, or until the okra is tender.
3. Serves four.

Extension Activity
Why do you think plantation owners, for the most part, preferred to keep their slaves illiterate (unable to read)? Share your ideas with your classmates.

Underground Railroad

The Underground Railroad was not a railroad in the true sense. Instead, it was a series of routes and safe houses that took runaway slaves to freedom in the North and in Canada. Runaway slaves escaping to the North were known as "passengers" or "freight." Places where they could stop and rest and receive meals were called "stations." Each station was run by a "stationmaster." A station might be a house or a church. It might also be a barn or any other place where slaves could hide and get help.

Between 1850 and the start of the Civil War, one of the most famous "conductors," Harriet Tubman, is said to have made 19 trips to the South. She helped more than 300 slaves to freedom in the "Promised Land." Numbered among her passengers on one trip were her aged parents. This brave women was referred to as the "Black Moses."

Project

Create a historical marker indicating a site along the route of the Underground Railroad.

Materials

- research materials
- poster board
- marker
- scissors

Directions

1. Familiarize yourself with historical markers. Many examples can be found on the Internet, in books, and in your own town or neighborhood.

2. Create a historical marker that might have appeared somewhere along the route of the Underground Railroad. Your marker might indicate the location of a particular trail, or it might identify a house, barn, church, or any other building used to house and feed runaway slaves in their flight to freedom.

3. Cut your poster board to resemble a typical historical marker. Then print what you think should appear on the marker. Use your imagination. Make up the name of a person whose house served as a "station" along the way, or give a name to a church or some other place.

Extension Activity

Make a list of railroad-like terms used in the Underground Railroad to confuse slave chasers, such as "conductors" and "stations." Explain what each meant. Compare your list with those of your classmates.

EP351 Black History © Highsmith® Inc. 2007

Sojourner Truth

She was almost six feet tall and as strong as most men. She also had a deep, masculine voice, which drew added attention to her. Although she took the name Sojourner Truth, her real name was Isabella Baumfree.

Sojourner Truth was a slave in New York for about 30 years. When that state outlawed slavery in 1827, she became a free woman. Soon she claimed to have had a vision in which God commanded her to travel the countryside and preach the gospel. She said that God also told her to change her name to Sojourner Truth. A "sojourner" is a person who travels, and "truth" implied that she was to preach Christianity wherever she went.

Sojourner walked through Long Island and Connecticut preaching the gospel. But she soon became active in both the anti-slavery and women's rights movements. She is particularly remembered for a speech she gave at the Women's Rights Convention in Akron, Ohio, in 1851. In her speech, she maintained that women were equal to men. When a man condescendingly maintained that women were inferior and "had to be helped into carriages and across ditches," she glared at him and flexed her arm muscles. "I have plowed, I have planted, and I have gathered into barns." In short, she was saying that she could do anything a man could. The crowd loved it, cheering wildly.

Project
Make a wall plaque honoring Sojourner Truth.

Materials
- piece of thin plywood or poster board
- saw (under adult supervision)
- sandpaper
- paint (water based)
- small paintbrush
- gold-colored paper
- glue or paste
- felt-tipped pen

Directions
1. With the help of an adult, cut a piece of thin plywood to 9 x 12 inches (23 x 30 cm). Sand smooth.
2. Paint the front and all sides of your piece of wood dark brown.
3. After the paint dries, cut a piece of gold paper to 8 x 11 inches (20 x 28 cm).
4. Center your piece of paper on the board and glue or paste in place.
5. With a felt-tipped pen, neatly print Sojourner Truth's name and other information you think should go on the plaque. Look at the information section for ideas.

Extension Activity
Pretend you are a newspaper reporter whose assignment is to interview Sojourner Truth following her speech at the Women's Rights Convention in Akron, Ohio, in 1851. What questions would you have asked her? How do you think she might have responded? Write a one-page paper detailing your interview.

The Abolitionist Movement

A move to end slavery in America began even before the United States became a nation. In 1784, Rhode Island became one of the first states to abolish, or end, slavery. Other northern states soon followed. By 1846, slavery was illegal throughout most of the North.

This was not true in the South. Large plantations made slavery desirable and profitable for southern growers. This led to the founding of the American Anti-Slavery Society in 1833. The goal of the society was the complete abolition of slavery. Some leading white abolitionists were William Lloyd Garrison, Theodore Weld, and Lucretia Mott. The most influential black abolitionist was Frederick Douglass (pictured at left), who had been a slave and could speak of slavery's evils firsthand.

Abolitionists published anti-slavery literature and spoke at anti-slavery rallies. Often they faced violence and sometimes death, especially in the South. Their efforts helped spark the Civil War and led to the declaration of the Emancipation Proclamation in 1863.

Project

Pretend you are living in the North in the years leading up to the Civil War. Make a wall poster advertising an upcoming lecture (talk) by a leading abolitionist.

Materials

- poster board
- markers
- felt-tipped pen
- crayons, colored pencils, or tempera paint
- brush, if paint is used

Directions

1. Use a magic marker and give your poster a heading in large capital letters.

2. In the middle of your poster, draw a picture of an abolitionist speaker. Color or paint your picture.

3. Using a felt-tipped pen, include the details concerning the speech: date, site, topic, speaker, etc.

Extension Activity

Write a one-page report on one of the abolitionists mentioned above.

The 54th Massachusetts Regiment

Unless you have seen the movie *Glory*, you may not be familiar with the 54th Massachusetts Regiment. What made this regiment (army group) so different at the time was that it was made up of all black soldiers. And these soldiers distinguished themselves in battle as few whites thought they could.

The 54th Massachusetts was organized in 1863. It was put under the command of Col. Robert Gould Shaw, a white officer. After training for three months, the regiment traveled to the coast of South Carolina. There it was assigned the task of taking Fort Wagner, a Confederate stronghold that guarded the city of Charleston.

On July 18, 1863, the regiment charged across the sand dunes to attack the fort. Almost half of the regiment, including Col. Shaw, lost their lives as Confederates fired from the top of the walls. A handful reached the fort's gates and engaged in hand-to-hand combat with the Confederates, but they failed to take the fort.

The action of the 54th Massachusetts on that historic evening proved beyond a doubt that black soldiers could fight as well and were just as brave as white soldiers. Sergeant William H. Carney, who fought at Fort Wagner, became the first African American soldier to be awarded the Medal of Honor.

Project

Army regiments throughout history have had their own regimental or battle flag. The all-black 54th Massachusetts was no exception. With this in mind, design a flag of your own.

Materials

- resource materials
- construction paper
- crayons or colored pencils
- pen

Directions

1. Pretend that your school is an army regiment. Design a flag that includes images or words that represent your school, community, city, or state. Look up battle flags in an encyclopedia or on the Internet for ideas.

2. Neatly draw your images and print your words (perhaps your school's motto) on a sheet of light-colored construction paper. Use your imagination.

3. Color your flag. Make the field, or background, a lighter color than the image(s) you include.

4. Explain your flag's design to your classmates.

Extension Activity

Pretend that you are a soldier in the 54th Massachusetts. Make an entry in your diary the night before the attack on Fort Wagner, expressing your thoughts and feelings.

Black Codes

The end of the Civil War brought freedom to the slaves of the South. But, in truth, they were not really free. Southern governments passed laws to keep freed slaves "in their place." These laws were called Black Codes. They varied from place to place, but in general they included some of the following:

- Blacks could not own property or testify in court; buy and sell goods; learn to read and write; own firearms; strike a white person; vote or hold office; or hold public meetings.
- Blacks had to remove their hats and stand at attention when a white person passed. They also had to stand off the sidewalk when a white woman came by.
- Blacks had to be off the streets after sundown.
- If a black person wanted to move about and visit someone, they had to have a pass to do so.

Black Codes also required all freed slaves to work. This usually meant that they continued farm work for the same planters who had owned them as slaves. Any black found not working faced arrest.

Project

Create a time capsule.

Materials

- box or any other container that could serve as a time capsule
- marker to label your box
- selected time capsule items

Directions

1. Pretend you are a freed slave living in the deep South after the Civil War. Think of things to place in a time capsule so that future generations would have a better idea of what life was like living under the Black Codes. Such items might include pictures, pieces of clothing, letters (some freed slaves could write), etc.
2. Share the contents of your capsule with your classmates.

Extension Activity

The Black Codes ended when federal troops began to occupy the South shortly after the Civil War. Later, to maintain their policy of segregation, most southern states passed what were called "Jim Crow" Laws. Look up the Jim Crow laws and write a paragraph explaining them.

EP351 Black History © Highsmith® Inc. 2007

Bill Pickett

Many people probably do not know that a large number of western cowboys were African Americans. One of the most famous was Bill Pickett.

Bill Pickett was a genuine ranch cowboy. Pictures show him dressed in the usual cowboy garb, complete with chaps. (Chaps are leather pants cowboys wear over their blue jeans to protect their legs from thorns and other hazards.) But Bill Pickett was more than just a regular cowboy. He became a rodeo performer, gaining fame for his unusual method of wrestling a longhorn steer to the ground.

In years past, ranchers used bulldogs to subdue cattle. A bulldog would clamp down on the upper lip of a steer to subdue him. This method was called "bulldogging." Bill Pickett copied this method with great success. He would grab a steer by the horns, clamp down on its upper lip with his teeth, and wrestle it to the ground. The animal would stop resisting.

Project
Make a pair of cowboy chaps.

Materials
- brown wrapping paper
- brown grocery bag
- stapler
- markers or crayons

Directions
1. Cut two strips of brown paper about 14 inches wide and the length of your leg.
2. Measure your waist. Then make a waistband out of a grocery bag. Cut it 8 inches wide and then fold it in half to make it stronger.
3. Staple the two strips of brown wrapping paper to your waistband. Decorate your chaps to give them a western design.
4. Wear your chaps over your jeans like a real cowboy.

Extension Activity
Why do you think many blacks migrated to the West in the years after the Civil War? Put your thoughts into a paragraph.

Booker T. Washington

Booker T. Washington was a black educator who is remembered for founding what became known as the Tuskegee Institute in Alabama. Washington started the vocational school in 1881 so that African American students could learn a useful trade. His belief was that blacks could better themselves by becoming self-sufficient and by not having to rely on others for help. His beliefs brought him into direct conflict with other black leaders, who thought that blacks could only attain equality by political means.

Washington began his school with 30 students in an old church building that leaked. But Tuskegee eventually grew to have an enrollment of 1,500 students and a campus containing some 100 buildings. There, in addition to taking academic subjects, students could receive training in such vocational areas as carpentry, farming, dairying, sewing, cooking, printing, and shoemaking.

Because he did not advocate complete equality for blacks, Washington won the support of many whites. He even became an informal adviser to presidents. Many blacks, however, referred to him as an "Uncle Tom."

Project
Make a collage.

Materials
- magazines, catalogs, and newspapers
- scissors
- glue
- poster board or large piece of paper

Directions
1. Cut pictures from magazines, catalogs, and newspapers to illustrate vocational courses taught at the Tuskegee Institute. Look for pictures that will serve to illustrate carpentry, printing, shoemaking, sewing, cooking, farming, and dairying.

2. Arrange the pictures in an interesting pattern on your poster board. Glue in place.

Extension Activity
What do you think some blacks meant when they referred to Booker T. Washington as an "Uncle Tom"?

The Harlem Renaissance

In the years following World War I, thousands of southern blacks pulled up stakes and moved north. They relocated to northern cities seeking jobs and a better way of life. Blacks in the North could vote and they experienced less discrimination than those in the South. This movement of African Americans to the North is referred to as the Great Migration.

Many blacks who moved north settled in the New York City district of Harlem. There they were joined by blacks from Africa, Puerto Rico, Haiti, Cuba, and Jamaica. From this large gathering of black people sprang what came to be called the Harlem Renaissance. The Harlem Renaissance was an outpouring of black achievements in art, literature, music, and theater. There were even noted achievements in science, as in the case of George Washington Carver, whose experiments with the simple peanut and sweet potato led to more than 400 useful products. Although Carver taught at the Tuskegee Institute in Alabama and did not move to the north, he is still considered a part of the Harlem Renaissance.

In literature, some outstanding black authors of the time were Langston Hughes, Nella Larson, James Weldon Johnson, Zora Neale Hurston, and Countee Cullen. Leading musicians and composers included the likes of Duke Ellington, W. C. Handy, Louis "Satchmo" Armstrong, and Scott Joplin. Josephine Baker, Billie Holiday, Bill "Bojangles" Robinson, Bessie Smith, and Charles Gilpin excelled as singers and stage performers. Artists included Aaron Douglas, Lois Jones, and William Henry Johnson.

In addition to the many achievements made by black artists, musicians, and others, the Harlem Renaissance was important for another reason. It helped open doors for blacks in other areas, such as sports.

Project #1
Make a mobile.

Materials
- large clothes hanger
- small index cards
- paper or larger index card
- felt-tipped pen
- crayons or colored pencils
- hole punch
- string

Directions
1. On the front of each index card, draw a picture of a famous African American writer, musician, or artist associated with the Harlem Renaissance.
2. On the back of each card, write the person's name and identify him or her as an artist, writer, musician, scientist, etc.
3. Punch a hole at the top of each card.
4. Cut pieces of string and tie cards at different lengths on the clothes hanger.
5. Make a sign on a piece of paper or larger index card to attach at the top of the hanger. Think of a title for your sign (Famous African Americans, Personalities of the Harlem Renaissance, etc.)

The Harlem Renaissance

Project #2

Write a one-page report on the Harlem Renaissance.

Materials

- pen or pencil

Directions

Use the space below to write a report on one of the artists, musicians, poets, or authors of the Harlem Renaissance.

_____

_____

_____

_____

_____

_____

_____

_____

_____

_____

_____

_____

_____

_____

_____

_____

_____

_____

_____

_____

_____

_____

_____

_____

_____

EP351 Black History © Highsmith® Inc. 2007

Blacks in World War II

In spite of prejudice and discrimination at home, African Americans served with honor in World War II. Most were drafted into the army, but others served in the navy, the army air corps, and the merchant marines. More than a few emerged as true heroes.

Before the Japanese sank the *USS Arizona* at Pearl Harbor on December 7, 1941, an African American cook named Dorie Miller rushed on deck and shot down several enemy planes. For his bravery, he was awarded the Navy Cross.

In the predawn hours of April 5 and 6, 1945, while charging a hill near Viareggio, Italy, Lieutenant Vernon Baker knocked out two German bunkers and a machine gun nest. He killed nine of the enemy in the process. Because of strong prejudice against African American servicemen, he had to wait 52 years to receive the Congressional Medal of Honor, the highest military award in America.

Although African Americans in the regular service were forced to serve in segregated units, those in the Merchant Marines started to both sail and work side-by-side with white Marines. A few even became captains of their own ships. The first African American Merchant Marine to command an integrated crew was Hugh Mulzac, who captained the *Booker T. Washington*. He made 22 trips across the Atlantic, ferrying troops and supplies overseas.

Sgt. Edward A. Carter Jr., although wounded five times, was still able to fight and capture two Germans. He was able to gather valuable information from his prisoners.

Private George Watson was aboard a ship that was sunk by enemy bombs in 1943. Instead of trying to save himself, he swam back and forth among wounded comrades helping them into rafts. He drowned when he was dragged down by the tow of the sinking ship.

Finally there were the Tuskegee Airmen. They were pilots of the all-black 332 Fighter Group. They were known as the Tuskegee Airmen because they had trained near the town of Tuskegee, Alabama. This group flew more than 1,500 missions escorting bombers to their targets. Although 66 of their pilots were killed, not a single bomber they were assigned to escort was ever shot down.

Project
Make a story cube about famous blacks in World War II.

Materials
- small, square box
- white paper
- crayons or colored pencils
- scissors
- glue, paste, or clear tape

Directions
1. Cut paper to fit on all sides of your box. Draw and color six pictures depicting African American heroes of World War II.
2. Glue, paste, or tape your pictures in place.

James Farmer

In 1998, James Farmer received the Presidential Medal of Freedom from President Bill Clinton. The Presidential Medal of Freedom is the highest award given to a civilian for service to his or her country. Farmer received the award for his work in the civil rights movement.

James Farmer graduated from the Howard University School of Religion in 1941. But the ministry was not to be his life's work. Instead, he became deeply involved in the struggle to end discrimination against blacks in America. In 1942, he and five others founded C.O.R.E., the Congress of Racial Equality. This organization sought to end segregation through nonviolent means. Like Martin Luther King Jr. some 20 years later, Farmer stressed peaceful acts of disobedience like those taught by Mahatma Gandhi, the great leader of India's independence following World War II.

Farmer served as director of C.O.R.E. until 1965 when he resigned. He believed that the organization was getting away from its policy of nonviolence and becoming too militant in its activities.

Project
Make a drawing of the Presidential Medal of Freedom.

Materials
- research materials
- white paper
- crayons or colored pencils

Directions
1. Find a picture of the Presidential Medal of Freedom in a book or on the Internet.
2. Draw your own picture of the medal, reproducing the exact colors.
3. At the bottom of your drawing, write a brief description of what each part of the medal represents.

Extension Activity
In 1947, C.O.R.E. sponsored an early version of the Freedom Ride through the upper South that met with very little resistance. In comparison, why do you think the Freedom Rides through the deep south in 1961 sparked so much violence?

EP351 Black History © Highsmith® Inc. 2007

Jackie Robinson

Jackie Robinson must have been quite nervous that afternoon of April 15, 1947. That was the day he played his first game for the Brooklyn Dodgers. It was also the day in which a black player first played in the major leagues of baseball.

Born in Georgia in 1919, Jackie Robinson went on to become a great athlete at UCLA in California. From 1942 to 1945, he served in the U.S. Army. He was a determined figure from the start. When he was having trouble getting his application accepted at Officer Training School, Jackie turned to the great boxing champion Joe Louis for help. Louis intervened and got Robinson and 14 other black men admitted to the school.

After World War II, Robinson played for the Kansas City Monarchs of the Negro American League. His skills caught the attention of major league owners, and he was soon playing for Montreal. Montreal was a minor league club of the Brooklyn Dodgers (now the Los Angeles Dodgers). In 1947, he was brought up to Brooklyn, where he became the major league's first black player.

Playing in the major leagues was at first difficult for Jackie Robinson. He was jeered and taunted everywhere he went. Many white players threatened to quit baseball rather than play on the same field with him. But he endured it all, and went on to become a great player. In 1947, he was voted major league rookie of the year.

Project #1
Make a cereal box report of a famous black baseball player.

Materials
- research materials
- empty cereal box, or any similar-size box
- white paper
- glue or paste
- felt-tipped pen
- ball-point pen
- crayons or colored pencils

Directions
1. Research another black athlete that played in the major leagues. Read about this player in an encyclopedia, book about baseball, or on the Internet.
2. Glue or paste white paper over all sides of the box, as well as the top and bottom.
3. On the top edge of the box, write the name of the baseball player on whom you are reporting.
4. On one side panel, write the team(s) for which your subject played.
5. On the other side panel, write the dates in which your subject played.
6. On the front of the box, draw a rough sketch of the player you have selected.
7. On the back of the box, write a brief account of your subject's accomplishments as a player.

Jackie Robinson

Project #1

Pretend you are Jackie Robinson, and write a letter to a friend.

Materials

- pen or pencil

Directions

1. Pretend that you are Jackie Robinson the night before his first major league baseball game. What is going through your mind?
2. Use the space below to write a short letter to a friend expressing your thoughts and feelings.

Date:

Dear _____,

_____

_____

_____

_____

_____

_____

_____

_____

_____

_____

Rosa Parks

Until a December day in 1955, Rosa Parks was an unknown seamstress in Montgomery, Alabama. Everyday she took a city bus to and from her job in a local department store. But what happened on that day made her a national figure.

On December 1 of that year, Rosa Parks boarded her usual bus home. She was doubly tired—tired from her day's work and tired of Jim Crow laws that required her to sit in the back of a bus, even when there were empty seats in the front. And she was tired of paying her fare at the front door of the bus and then having to walk around to the back of the bus to enter. On December 1 she entered the bus and sat down near the front. When she refused to give up her seat to a white man, she was arrested and taken to jail.

Rosa Parks's action on that day started a revolution of sorts in Montgomery. From December 1, 1955, to December 21, 1956, Montgomery's blacks boycotted the city buses. This meant that they refused to ride them. They either walked, took taxis, or formed car pools to get to where they were going. Their effort and determination resulted in the U.S. Supreme Court ruling that segregation on buses was unconstitutional.

Rosa Parks has often been called the "Mother of the Civil Rights Movement." She remained an active participant in the struggle for equal rights until her death in 2005.

Project

Make a television set out of a cardboard box and tell the story of the Montgomery bus boycott of 1955.

Materials

- cardboard box, about 12 x 7 inches (30.5 x 18 cm)
- scissors
- sheet of butcher paper
- pencil
- crayons or colored pencils
- small knife (use with adult supervision)

Directions

1. Cut the flaps or lids from the cardboard box. Turn the box upside down.
2. Using a small knife, cut out a small "screen" on one side of the box.
3. Cut a slit the width of the butcher paper on two sides of the box , slightly higher and lower than the screen.
4. Cut a piece from the butcher paper long enough to draw about 10 pictures that will fit the screen. Allow enough blank space to permit the length of paper to be inserted into one slit and pulled through to the other.
5. Draw and color 10 pictures that help to tell the story of the Montgomery bus boycott. Make each picture the size of the opening you cut for your screen. Draw a line separating the pictures. Give each picture a caption.
6. Pull your series of pictures through the screen to tell your story.

Rosa Parks/Montgomery Bus Boycott

Project

The effect of the Montgomery Bus Boycott was widespread. Take on the role of a person living at the time of the boycott and write a journal.

Materials

- plain writing or drawing paper
- colored pencils, markers, crayons
- stapler

Directions

1. Staple four sheets of writing paper together to form a booklet.
2. Choose from the list of people below or come up with your own identity.
   - an African American who takes the bus to work in Montgomery
   - a white bus driver in Montgomery
   - a Montgomery, Alabama, business owner
   - a member of the Women's Political Council
   - an African American living in Baton Rouge, Louisiana
   - a family member of any of the above
   - a minister
   - a reporter
3. As this person, write one week of journal entries. Include facts as well as your thoughts and feelings about the boycott. How did your daily routines change? How did the boycott affect your work? How did it affect your family, friends, and neighbors? On the last day of your journal, tell what you think will happen next. What might have to happen to bring the boycott to an end?
4. Decorate the cover of your journal.

EP351 Black History © Highsmith® Inc. 2007

Dr. Martin Luther King Jr.

A study of the struggle by African Americans to gain equal rights almost has to begin with a discussion of Dr. Martin Luther King Jr. Many people would agree that this southern Baptist minister became the heart and soul of the civil rights movement.

Martin Luther King was relatively unknown until the Montgomery bus boycott of 1955. That incident thrust him into the limelight. He soon became a recognized leader who urged black people to use non-violent means to win their rights.

Dr. King and other black leaders formed the Southern Christian Leadership Conference in 1957. This group coordinated civil rights activities during the 1950s and 1960s. Through it all, King continued to urge blacks to follow a policy of non-violence. Although they were often beaten and sometimes killed, most blacks who actively participated in the civil rights movement did not fight back.

Dr. King led the struggle for civil rights until his assassination in 1968. His leadership resulted in the Civil Rights Act of 1964 and the Voting Rights Act of 1965. At the time of his death, most Jim Crow laws had been struck down and America's blacks had come ever closer to realizing full equality.

Project

Make a K-W-L Chart about Dr. Martin Luther King Jr.

Materials

- Dr. Martin Luther King Jr. K-W-L Chart
- felt-tipped pen

Directions

1. Chart your learning experience using the K-W-L Chart.
2. Under the column headed "K," neatly print what you know about Dr. Martin Luther King Jr.
3. Under the column labeled "W," print what you want or expect to learn from your research.
4. Read more about Dr. Martin Luther King Jr. in an encyclopedia or other source.
5. Under the column headed "L," print what you learned from reading about Dr. King.

For the Teacher

Copy one K-W-L Chart (page 24) per student.

Extension Activity

Dr. Martin Luther King Jr. adhered to (followed) the non-violent principles taught by Mahatma Gandhi of India. Look up Gandhi in an encyclopedia and write a one-page report on his life.

Dr. Martin Luther King Jr.

What you already know about Dr. King.	**What you want or expect to learn about Dr. King.**	**What you learned about Dr. King.**
K	W	L

Showdown at Central High

In 1954, the U.S. Supreme Court ruled that segregated schools were unconstitutional. The first real test of the ruling, however, did not take place until 1957.

The scene was Central High School in Little Rock, Arkansas. On the morning of September 23, nine African American students attempted to enter the school. Violence broke out, and a number of people were injured, including several reporters and photographers. The next day, President Dwight D. Eisenhower ordered paratroopers to Little Rock to restore order.

Life at Central High was difficult for the nine black students. They were constant victims of racial slurs and jeers. Soldiers had to escort them to class and protect them on campus. Neither threats nor harassment, however, dampened their determination. That spring, Ernest Green, the only senior among the group, became the first African American student to graduate from the school. He, like the others, had endured a lot for nine months, but he never wavered from his goal.

In the hope of preventing further integration, Governor Orval Faubus decided to close all of Little Rock's high schools for the following year. But the U.S. Supreme Court ruled that a state could not take such action to avoid integration. So all of the city's schools were forced to open their doors to African American students. Soon, cities in other states did the same, and school segregation became a thing of the past.

Project #1
Make a congratulatory card for Ernest Green.

Directions
1. Fold a sheet of construction paper in half to create a card.
2. On the outside of your card, neatly print a heading. Then draw and color a picture associated with graduation. Color your picture, using either crayons or colored pencils.
3. On the inside of your card, write a congratulatory note to Ernest Green. Be creative—say a little more than just "congratulations!"

Materials
- sheet of white or colored construction paper
- ruler
- scissors
- pencil or pen
- crayons or colored pencils

Ernest Green

Project #2

When Ernest Green walked onto the stage and received his high school diploma during graduation ceremonies at Central High School, he knew many people were against him. How do you think Ernest felt? Do you think it bothered him? Pretend you are Ernest Green on graduation day.

Materials
- pen or pencil

Directions

In the space below, write your thoughts as if you were Ernest Green on his graduation day.

_____

_____

_____

_____

_____

_____

_____

_____

_____

_____

_____

_____

_____

_____

_____

_____

_____

Lunch Counter Sit-Ins

Can you imagine anyone today—regardless of race—being refused service in a restaurant or at a lunch counter? But that is what happened to African Americans in the South before the passage of a new civil rights act in 1964.

To fight against discrimination in public places, blacks devised a new tactic: the sit-in. This tactic was first used in 1960, in Greensboro, North Carolina. On February 1 of that year, four black students from North Carolina A&T State University in Greensboro entered the local Woolworth store and sat down at the counter. They ordered lunch. They were refused service, but they sat there until the store closed.

The following day, the four black students were joined by others. Soon there were hundreds participating in the sit-in. Some were white. Despite being arrested, beaten, and sprayed with food, they sat in shifts at the lunch counter. Others did the same at the Kress store down the street. Soon, sit-ins spread to other cities and states in the South. Besides lunch counters, sit-ins were staged in parks, restaurants, swimming pools, and other public places. Such tactics helped break down racial barriers in the upper South. But as events would soon prove, ending segregation in public places in the deep South would not be easy.

For the Teacher

Project #1
Have students prepare and present a simulated interview.

Materials
- pen and paper for student reports
- props for broadcast presentation, such as a video camera and handheld microphone

Directions

1. Have students pretend they are newspaper reporters. Have them "interview" one of the black students sitting at the lunch counter of the Woolworth store in Greensboro, North Carolina, the person working behind the counter, or one of the curious bystanders looking in from outside the store. Assign these interviews or allow students to choose.
2. Have students write at least one page of an interview.
3. Provide props and have students report on their interviews as if they are giving a television broadcast.

Lunch Counter Sit-ins

Project #2

On February 27, 1960, blacks who were staging a sit-in in Nashville, Tennessee, were attacked by a group of whites. Soon the police arrived to stop the fighting. But then a strange thing happened: instead of arresting the whites who were assaulting the sit-in participants, the police arrested the blacks, charging them with "disorderly conduct." Write your thoughts about what happened that day.

Materials

- pen or pencil

Directions

Use the space below to write your thoughts about the Nashville sit-in. What does the situation tell you about the police in some parts of the South at that time? Why do you think this was so?

EP351 Black History © Highsmith® Inc. 2007

Freedom Riders

In Anniston, Alabama, a bus was set afire and its passengers beaten. In Birmingham, a passenger was kicked unconscious. And at the Greyhound bus station in Montgomery, another rider was beaten so severely that he needed more than 50 stitches to close his wounds.

The above attacks occurred as a result of the Freedom Rides of 1961. These rides were the idea of James Farmer of C.O.R.E., the Congress of Racial Equality. Farmer reasoned that if whites and blacks together attempted to integrate restrooms and other facilities at bus stations in the deep south, they would be met with violence. He was right. He also thought that such violence would lead to the federal government stepping in and ending segregation in interstate travel and at bus station facilities. He was right there, too. But the civil rights activists who came to be called Freedom Riders paid a price for their courage and determination.

The first group of Freedom Riders left Washington, D.C., on May 4, 1961. Their destination was New Orleans, Louisiana. There were 13 young people—seven blacks and six whites—aboard the bus that departed the capital's bus station and headed south. At each stop along the way, the blacks planned to use the "White Only" restrooms, while the whites would use those marked "Colored Only." Throughout the trip, the black riders would sit in the front of the bus, while the white riders would sit in the back.

The group met resistance in Virginia, and encountered violence in the Carolinas and Georgia. When the bus reached Atlanta, the group divided. One group took a bus bound for Anniston, Alabama, while the other boarded a bus for Birmingham. Both groups were attacked upon reaching their destination. Those who had gone to Birmingham later took another bus to Montgomery. They met with violence there also.

The Freedom Riders failed in their plan to ride all the way to New Orleans. But they succeeded in their overall goal. Because of their efforts, the federal government made segregation in interstate travel illegal.

For the Teacher

Project
Copy one Freedom Riders page (page 30) per student.

Freedom Riders

Complete both projects below to gain a deeper understanding of the events surrounding the Freedom Rides.

Project #1

Write a letter to the president.

Materials

- stationery or notebook paper
- pencil

Directions

Pretend that you were a student at the time of the Freedom Rides. Write a letter to President John F. Kennedy expressing your feelings and what you think the federal government should do to address the violence that resulted from the rides.

Project #2

Materials

- pen or pencil

Directions

Knowing that you faced danger and possibly bodily harm, would you have volunteered to be a Freedom Rider in 1961? Why or why not? List several reasons in the space below.

_____

_____

_____

_____

_____

_____

_____

_____

_____

_____

_____

_____

_____

_____

James Meredith

On October 1, 1962, James Meredith made history. In spite of efforts by Mississippi Governor Ross Barnett to keep him out, Meredith became the first African American in the state to attend the University of Mississippi at Oxford, also known as Ole Miss. His first day of class came almost two years after he had originally applied for admission.

After having served nine years in the United States Air Force, Meredith enrolled at Jackson State College in Jackson, Mississippi. He studied at the all-black school for two years and then applied for admission to Ole Miss. The date was January 31, 1961. On February 4, his request to be admitted was denied. On May 31, he took his case to court. A ruling dragged out until September 10, 1962. On that date the U.S. Supreme Court ordered the university to accept his application.

In the following two weeks, the situation at Ole Miss grew intense. On September 25, 1962, Governor Barnett personally blocked Meredith's entrance to the university. Five days later, on September 30, riots broke out. President John F. Kennedy ordered 16,000 federal troops and a number of federal marshals to Oxford. Shots were fired, and two people were killed. More than 100 marshals were wounded. Order was finally restored, and James Meredith attended his first class at the school on October 1.

James Meredith successfully broke the color barrier at the college level in the South. Other universities in other southern states would follow and open their doors to African American students.

Project
Make an illustrated time line.

Materials
- butcher paper
- felt-tipped pen or marker
- pencil
- crayons or colored pencils

Directions
1. On butcher paper, use a felt-tipped marker to write the dates and events of James Meredith's Ole Miss experience.
2. Beneath each date and event, draw and color a picture illustrating it.
3. Ask your teacher to display your time line on a bulletin board or wall.

Extension Activity
James Meredith's story did not end with his admission to Ole Miss, nor did it end with his graduation from the university in 1964. His life took several strange turns afterwards. With this in mind, research his life from 1964 onward in an encyclopedia or on the Internet. Write a one-page report on your findings.

Fannie Lou Hamer

Fannie Lou Hamer was a brave woman. Once she was beaten so badly that her kidneys and one eye were permanently damaged. This came after she registered to vote in Mississippi and tried to help others do the same. As a final blow, she was evicted from (kicked off) the farm on which she was a sharecropper.

Ms. Hamer became involved in the civil rights movement in 1962. In that year, workers from several civil rights organizations came to Mississippi to help black people register to vote. Even after being beaten and evicted from her farm, Fannie Lou joined in their efforts. In 1964, she and others formed the Mississippi Freedom Democratic Party. They organized the party in opposition to the white-dominated Democratic Party of Mississippi. They sent delegates to the Democratic National Convention that year, and although they were not recognized as official delegates, their actions brought worldwide attention to the voting problem in Mississippi.

Fannie Lou Hamer continued her work in the civil rights movement until her death in 1977. Although she had only a sixth-grade education, she received several honorary college degrees for her contributions.

Project
Make a bookmark honoring Fannie Lou Hamer.

Materials
- poster board or card stock
- pen or pencil; colored pencils or crayons
- scissors
- hole punch
- clear contact paper
- ribbon

Directions
1. Draw the outline of your bookmark on poster board or card stock.
2. Cut out your bookmark. On the front, draw a sketch of Fannie Lou Hamer. (You can find sample pictures in books or on the Internet.)

On the back, neatly print a sentence or two highlighting Fannie Lou Hamer's role in the civil rights movement.

3. Use colored pencils or crayons to decorate both sides. Cover both sides with clear contact paper.
4. Punch a hole in the top of your bookmark and insert a colorful ribbon.

Extension Activity
You have read that Fannie Lou Hamer was a sharecropper. Look up the sharecropper system in an encyclopedia and write a paragraph explaining it.

EP351 Black History © Highsmith® Inc. 2007

The March on Washington

They came to Washington on planes. They came on trains and buses. Some walked. One man reportedly roller-skated all the way from Chicago. And legend has it that an elderly gentleman rode his bicycle to the nation's capital from Ohio.

The date was August 28, 1963. Some 250,000 people had come to Washington, D.C., for a peaceful demonstration. The large throng gathered to support an important civil rights bill that President John Kennedy had submitted to Congress. Of the 250,000 participants, more than 50,000 were white. Movie stars marched along with garbage collectors.

The highlight of the day was Dr. Martin Luther King's "I have a dream" speech in front of the Lincoln Memorial. Part of his speech included this now-famous statement: "I have a dream that my four little children will one day live in a nation where they will not be judged by the color of their skin but by the content of their character."

Project #1
Create a shoe box diorama depicting a scene from the March on Washington.

Materials
- large shoebox
- construction paper or plain copy paper
- markers, crayons, or watercolors and paintbrush
- modeling clay
- small figurines
- glue
- scissors

Directions
1. Place the shoebox on its side so that the bottom can be used for the background.
2. Draw a scene for the background of your diorama on a piece of paper. The scene might consist of the skyline and the crowd of people gathered at the Washington Monument or the Lincoln Memorial. Continue the scene on both the inside sides of the box.
3. If your diorama depicts a scene of the crowd at the Washington Monument, create a replica of the famous monument out of modeling clay. If your choice of scene is the Lincoln Memorial where Dr. King gave his "I have a dream" speech, make a replica of the Lincoln Memorial.
4. If your diorama includes Dr. King speaking, use a small figurine for his likeness, or create your own out of modeling clay. Do the same for other demonstrators.

The March on Washington

Project #2

In his "I have a dream" speech, Dr. King said that he hoped that someday his children would be judged by the "content of their character" and not by the "color of their skin." Do you think his dream has come true? In the chart below, list the ways you think his dream has or has not been realized.

EP351 Black History © Highsmith® Inc. 2007

Freedom Summer

It was supposed to be a summer when blacks in Mississippi were to receive help in filling out registration forms and young black children would be taught to read. But before it really got started, tragedy struck.

On the evening of June 21, 1964, three young civil rights workers drove out to inspect the damage to a black church near Philadelphia, Mississippi. The church had been burned, no doubt, because it was to be the location of the first Freedom School to instruct young black children. The three young workers were James Chaney, Andrew Goodman, and Michael Schwerner. Chaney was a local African American from nearby Meridian. Goodman and Schwerner were young whites from New York. As they surveyed the damage to the church, they had no idea of the fate that awaited them.

While driving back toward the town of Philadelphia, the three civil rights workers were stopped by the local police and charged with speeding. They were taken to jail and held for several hours. During their time in jail, local members of the Ku Klux Klan were planning their murders. Since the sheriff who made the arrest was a Klansman, nothing stood in the way of the plotters to carry out their murderous deed.

When Chaney, Goodman, and Schwerner were released from jail, they sensed their lives were in danger. They got back in their car and tried to make it to the Alabama border. But they were followed by Klansmen in several cars and were once again stopped. This time they were dragged from their vehicle and killed. Goodman and Schwerner were shot, while Chaney was beaten to death. A bulldozer operator who was also a member of the Klan, and who had earlier dug a deep ditch, covered their bodies under an earthen dam.

Six weeks passed before the grave of the three young men was discovered. After many months, 21 men were arrested and 19 were charged with being involved in the murders. Seven were sent to prison, one of whom was the deputy sheriff who had arrested the three young men.

Project #1

Write a commemorative poem. (Commemorative means "to honor or remember.")

Materials

- printer or copy paper
- construction paper
- pen or pencil
- glue

Directions

1. On a sheet of plain white paper, write a short commemorative poem honoring the three young civil rights workers who were murdered in June 1964.

2. Cut a frame out of a sheet of construction paper.

3. Glue your poem to the back of the construction paper so that it resembles a picture in a frame.

4. Read your poem to the class.

Freedom Summer

Project #1

Many young civil rights workers were members of SNCC, the Student Non-Violent Coordinating Committee. Write a short paper about this organization.

Materials

- research materials
- pen or pencil

Directions

Do some research on the SNCC. Use the space below to write a short paper about this organization's founding and purpose.

_____
_____
_____
_____
_____
_____
_____
_____
_____
_____
_____
_____
_____
_____
_____
_____
_____
_____
_____
_____
_____
_____
_____
_____

EP351 Black History © Highsmith® Inc. 2007

The Civil Rights Act of 1964

Blacks in America came close to realizing their dream of equal rights when Congress passed the Civil Rights Act of 1964. In brief, this act forbid discrimination in all public places. It outlawed segregation in hotels, restaurants, theaters, hospitals, parks, and other facilities. It also created the Equal Employment Opportunity Commission, which made discrimination illegal in education and employment. After much opposition from some southern members of Congress, President Lyndon Johnson signed the act into law on July 2, 1964.

The Civil Rights Act of 1964 was much more effective than previous civil rights laws. This was because it authorized the Attorney General of the United States to withhold federal money from any program that practiced discrimination. The act failed, however, to guarantee blacks in the deep South the right to vote. That would come the following year, when the Voting Rights Act of 1965 made it unconstitutional to use literacy tests to prevent blacks from voting.

Project

Make a paper scroll.

Materials

- piece of butcher paper
- markers
- craft dowels
- glue

Directions

1. Cut a piece of butcher paper to 9 x 32 inches (23 x 81 cm).
2. Holding the paper vertically, print the highlights or main points of the Civil Rights Act of 1964, spacing the words so that most of the length is used.
3. Glue the top and bottom of your paper to a wooden dowel. When the glue dries, roll your scroll up.
4. Pretend you lived many years ago when news and announcements were read from scrolls. Read your scroll to your class.

Extension Activity

Why do you think some southern legislators fought against the passage of a strong civil rights bill?

From Selma to Montgomery

When they left Selma for the state capital in Montgomery on March 21, 1965, they numbered some 3,200 marchers. By the time they reached Montgomery four days later, their numbers had swelled to 25,000. "They" were the brave souls determined to end voting discrimination in Alabama and elsewhere.

The Civil Rights Act passed by Congress in 1964 did much to end discrimination against blacks in America. But it failed to address one major issue: the use of biased, subjective literacy tests to keep many African Americans from voting. The march from Selma to Montgomery was designed to help end this practice and ensure that all Americans were granted their constitutional right to vote.

Two previous attempts by blacks to march to the state capital had ended in failure. One attempt, on March 7 of the same year, was turned back with violence. No sooner had almost 600 marchers crossed the bridge leading from Selma than they were met by police. Television viewers across America were shocked to see marchers beaten and subjected to tear gas. These terrible acts of violence gave this date its infamous name "Bloody Sunday."

Two weeks later the march proceeded under the protection of regular troops and the Alabama National Guard. President Lyndon Johnson had ordered the military to accompany the marchers on the 54-mile journey to Montgomery. They arrived safely in the capital on March 25, where Dr. Martin Luther King Jr. addressed the crowd.

Almost four months after the Selma-to-Montgomery march, Congress passed the Voting Rights Act. of 1965. This act made literacy tests as a requirement for voting illegal. At long last, African Americans everywhere had won the right to vote.

Project #1

Make a placard, or sign, you would have carried had you participated in the Selma-to-Montgomery march.

Materials

- poster board
- markers or tempera paint
- small paintbrush
- stick or dowel
- thumbtacks, stapler, or glue

Directions

1. Think of a slogan or words to print on your placard. Use markers or tempera paint. Make your placard as eye-appealing as possible. Remember, you want onlookers to notice your message.

2. Attach your placard to a stick, using either thumb tacks, a stapler, or glue.

3. With your teacher's permission, join your classmates in a "march" around the classroom.

EP351 Black History © Highsmith® Inc. 2007

From Selma to Montgomery

Project #2
Draw a small map of Alabama.

Materials
- altas or encyclopedia
- white, unlined paper
- felt-tipped pen
- crayons or colored pencils

Directions
1. Using a map from an atlas or encyclopedia as reference, draw your own map of Alabama.
2. Label major cities on your map.
3. Draw a line indicating the route taken by the marchers on March 21–25.
4. Color your map.

Project #3
Write a letter to a friend.

Materials
- pen or pencil

Directions
Pretend you were on the Selma-to-Montgomery march. Use the space below to write a letter to a friend describing your experiences as you marched and camped out along the way.

Date: _____

Dear _____ ,

_____

_____

_____

_____

_____

_____

The Right to Vote—At Last!

On August 6, 1965, the Voting Rights Act was adopted. At that time, one-third of eligible blacks and two-thirds of eligible whites were registered to vote. The Voting Rights Act was written to enforce the Fifteenth Amendment, which stated that citizens could not be denied voting rights based on their color or race. Because the amendment did not specifically deny the use of other voting prerequisites, many African Americans still were not allowed to vote. The Voting Rights Act made it illegal for a state to use a literacy (reading and writing) test to keep people from voting.

The literacy tests given to voter applicants were very difficult, and were not necessarily equal for all applicants. A typical test, assigned by a registrar, consisted of reading and writing down a portion of the Constitution. Questions regarding that portion of the Constitution, as well as general questions about the American government, made up the remainder of the test. Completed tests were reviewed by a board of registrars who decided whether or not the applicant "qualified." This sometimes meant that a black applicant answering all the questions correctly could still fail, while a white applicant with incorrect answers could still pass or might not have to take a test at all.

In addition to literacy tests, blacks were routinely harrassed and intimidated when attempting to vote. The Voting Rights Act also allowed for election observers to ensure everyone's right to vote.

Project
Create two literacy tests—one that is very simple, and one that is difficult. Give the test to your classmates.

Materials
- pen
- paper

Directions
1. Write two different tests. Make one test much more difficult. For example, a question on the easy test might be "Who is the current President of the United States?" while the difficult test might include, "Recite the preamble to the United States Constitution."

2. Make copies of your test.

3. Give the test to your classmates. You choose who will get the easy test, and who will get the hard test.

4. Decide what "rights" will be given or denied based on the test. Tell those taking the test what they will or will not be allowed to do based on their scores. For example, you might say those who don't pass won't get a lunch period.

4. Score the tests. Will you give rights to those who passed? Or will you decide, based on other reasons, who "passed"?

5. Have your classmates write down how they felt having to take this type of test.

EP351 Black History

Prejudice

Project

Why have various groups of minorities suffered from discrimination (unfair treatment), and sometimes outright hate, throughout America's history? What causes some people to be prejudiced toward a particular group? Consider the groups of people who have been discriminated against and explore how this discrimination has changed over time.

Materials

- pen or pencil

Directions

1. Fill in the chart below to explore how discrimation against various groups has changed over time.
2. On the left, make a list of groups that have experienced prejudice in America's history. In the middle column, list these experiences. In the right-hand column, describe whether or not society has changed and how.

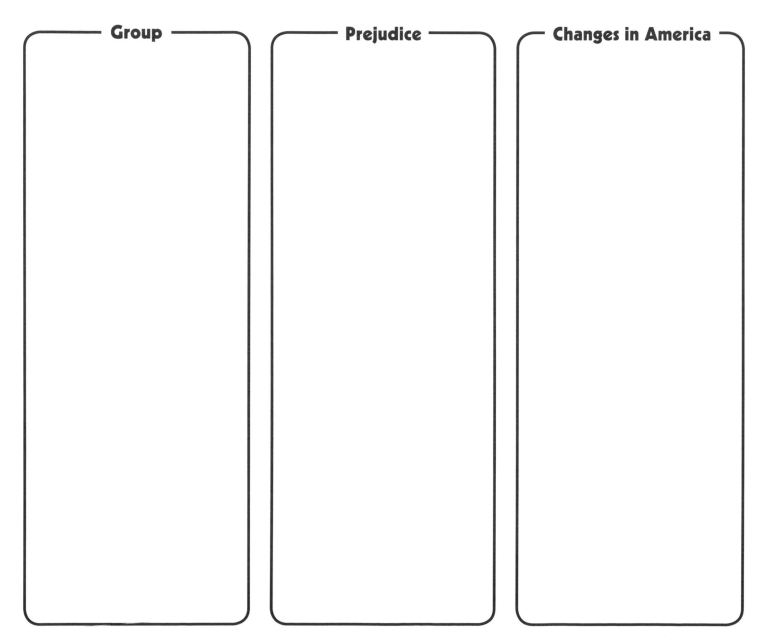

Group	Prejudice	Changes in America

The Watts Riot

Normally a routine traffic stop for reckless driving would not result in a riot. But that is what happened on the night of August 11, 1965. On that evening, a black person was arrested for drunk driving in the African American community of Watts in Los Angeles, California. Rumors spread of police brutality, and soon thousands of people were in the streets. Stores were fire bombed and looted, windows broken, and cars and buses set afire. By the time the National Guard restored order five days later, 34 people had been killed. More than 1,000 were injured, and hundreds of buildings were destroyed.

The Watts Riot resulted when frustration in the black communities of large American cities boiled over. That summer, and in succeeding summers, there were also riots in such places as Newark, Detroit, and Chicago. Although Dr. Martin Luther King Jr. had urged a policy of non-violence, such inner-city problems as unemployment, drug abuse, crime, and alcoholism caused some African Americans to turn to violence in hopes of achieving their ends.

Project

Pretend you are a newspaper reporter for *The Los Angeles Times* covering the Watts Riots of 1965. Write the lead paragraph to a story you will write, describing the events of the six days. Be sure to include in your paragraph answers to the five "W" questions (Who? What? When? Where? and Why?) that are characteristic of a good lead paragraph. Print the name of your newspaper at the top, along with the date and a headline for your story.

Materials

• newsprint or construction paper
• pencil
• sample newspaper to use as a guide

Directions

1. Print the name of the newspaper at the top of your paper in large letters.
2. Write the date below the name of the newspaper.
3. Print the headline to your story in letters slightly smaller than those used to write the name of the newspaper.
4. Write your lead paragraph.

Extension Activity
Is using violence to achieve a goal ever justified? Give reasons for your answers.

Thurgood Marshall

On June 13, 1967, Thurgood Marshall was appointed to become the first African American to serve as a justice on the U.S. Supreme Court. He was nominated to that position by President Lyndon B. Johnson.

As a child, Thurgood Marshall was headstrong and argumentative. His behavior sometimes got him in trouble with his teachers. As punishment, his elementary school principal would make him sit with a copy of the Constitution. He was not permitted to rejoin his class until he had memorized a part of that document.

Thurgood Marshall matured and went on to earn a law degree from Howard University in Washington, D.C. For many years he was a chief lawyer for the NAACP. His efforts led to the famous Supreme Court ruling of 1954 that declared segregated schools to be unconstitutional. He then served as a Court of Appeals judge and as Solicitor General of the United States. After being appointed to the Supreme Court, he served with distinction until health matters forced him to retire in 1991.

Project

Make a mandala. A mandala is a circle that is divided into four sections. Each section tells something about the person it pertains to.

Materials

- plain white paper
- pencil or pen
- crayons or colored pencils

Directions

1. Draw a circle about 6 inches in diameter on a piece of white paper. Using a ruler, divide the circle into 4 equal quarters.
2. In the upper left-hand quarter, draw a picture of Thurgood Marshall. (Look in an encyclopedia for an example.)

3. In the second, third, and fourth quarters of your mandala, draw pictures that illustrate something about Thurgood Marshall's life or career. (One picture might be of the Supreme Court.)
4. At the bottom of your mandala, briefly explain what each of your pictures stands for.

Extension Activity

Thurgood Marshall's first name was originally spelled "Thoroughgood." While still in elementary school, he convinced his parents to change it. Why do you think he objected to the original spelling?

Juneteenth

On June 19 each year, African Americans celebrate Juneteenth. The name of this festival comes from combining "June" and "nineteenth."

Juneteenth began in 1865. General Gordon Granger arrived in Galveston, Texas, on June 19 to inform the people there that the Civil War had ended two months earlier. News traveled slowly in those days, and plantation owners in Texas had never told their slaves about the Emancipation Proclamation that President Abraham Lincoln had issued in 1863 freeing all slaves. Various reasons are given for this delay. One is that plantation owners wanted their slaves to work on as many crops as possible before news of their freedom reached Texas.

Many activities are associated with the celebration of Juneteenth. There are parades, speakers, prayer services, and family reunions. There are also barbecues, ball games, rodeos, fishing, music, and dancing.

Project

Make a poster advertising a Juneteenth celebration. Show various activities connected with celebrating Juneteenth.

Materials

- poster board
- magazines, catalogs, newspapers
- paper
- scissors
- glue
- pen or pencil

Directions

1. Find and cut out pictures in magazines, catalogs, and newspapers that serve to illustrate activities that are part of Juneteenth. If you can't find pictures for some events, draw these on paper and cut them out to be part of your collage.

2. Arrange your pictures in a collage on poster board. Glue in place.

Extension Activity

Juneteenth is a state holiday in Texas. Do you think it should be declared a national holiday? Why or why not? Put your thoughts into a paragraph and share them with your classmates.

EP351 Black History © Highsmith® Inc. 2007

Celebrating Kwanzaa

Kwanzaa is a week-long celebration observed by many African Americans. It takes place between December 26 and New Year's Day. It is not a substitute for Christmas or any other religious celebration. It is a time when African Americans celebrate their history, culture, and traditions. Emphasis is placed on such values as family, community responsibility, and self-improvement. Kwanzaa means "first fruits."

Kwanzaa was created in 1966 by Dr. Ron "Maulana" Karenga, a professor at California State University. It is based on seven principles. One principle is stressed on each day of the holiday. These principles, in their English translation, are: Unity, Self-Determination, Collective Work and Responsibility, Cooperative Economics, Purpose, Creativity, and Faith.

Project
Make a chart of the seven principles of Kwanzaa.

Materials
- poster board
- marker
- reference materials

Directions
1. At the top of your poster board, neatly print in large letters "Seven Principles of Kwanzaa."
2. Divide your chart into two columns. The left column should not be as wide as the right column. Label this column "Principle." Under this heading, neatly print the seven principles.
3. Use reference materials to find the African (Swahili) word for the seven principles. Write these words in parentheses next to the English words.
4. In the right column of your chart, print a brief explanation of each principle.

Extension Activity
How is Kwanzaa similar in some ways to the Jewish celebration of Hanukkah? Consult an encyclopedia for comparisons.

Kwanzaa Kinaras

The celebration of Kwanzaa is centered around a number of symbols. One is the *kinara*, or candle holder. The kinara contains seven candles, one of which is lighted for each of the seven days of Kwanzaa. Three candles are red in color, three are green, and one is black. The black candle, which is placed in the middle of the kinara, stands for black people. The three red candles placed on the left represent the blood shed by black people in their struggles. The three green candles placed on the right side of the kinara stand for hope and the color of the motherland.

Project

Create a kinara candle holder with seven candles.

Materials

- red, green, black, yellow, brown, and blue construction paper
- glue
- scissors

Directions

1. Cut a candle holder from brown construction paper. Make it about 12 x 6 inches (30.5 x 15 cm). You decide the shape of your candle holder.

2. Glue your candle holder in place near the bottom of the sheet of blue construction paper.

3. Draw and cut out one candle from the black construction paper about 6 x1 inch (15 x 2.5 cm). Glue it in place at the center of your candle holder.

4. Draw and cut out three candles from the red construction paper. Make them the same size as the black candle. Glue all three in place to the left of the black candle.

5. Draw and cut out three candles from the green construction paper. Glue all three in place to the right of the black candle.

6. Cut small pieces resembling flames from the yellow construction paper. Glue them to the top of the seven candles.

Extension Activity

You now know the purpose of a Kwanzaa kinara, as well as what it looks like. Is its purpose similar to the Jewish Menorah, or is it quite different? Look up Menorah in an encyclopedia and make a note of similarities and differences.

Time Line

15th Century	European traders capture slaves from Africa's west coast
1770	The Boston Massacre occurs; Crispus Attucks and four others are killed in the fighting
1804	York, William Clark's personal slave, accompanies Lewis and Clark on their exploration of the Louisiana Territory
1833	The American Anti-Slavery Society is founded
1852	Harriet Beecher Stowe publishes *Uncle Tom's Cabin*
1863	The all-black 54th Massachusetts Regiment distinguishes itself in the attack on Fort Wagner in South Carolina
1865	Black Codes designed to deprive free blacks of their rights are passed in the South
1881	Booker T. Washington founds Tuskegee Institute in Alabama
1907	Bill Pickett begins his career as a rodeo performer
1919	The Harlem Renaissance, an outflowing of black achievements in art, literature, and music, begins in New York City
1941–1945	Numerous black servicemen fight bravely and win honors during World War II
1942	James Farmer helps found the Congress of Racial Equality
1947	Jackie Robinson becomes the first black person to play in the baseball major leagues
1955	Rosa Parks refuses to give up her seat on a Montgomery, Alabama, city bus, an act that helps start the civil rights movement
1957	Dr. Martin Luther King Jr. and other black leaders form the Southern Christian Leadership Conference
1957	Nine black students enroll at Central High School in Little Rock, Arkansas, signaling the end of school segregation in the South
1960	The first sit-in takes place at a Woolworth lunch counter in Greensboro, North Carolina
1961	Freedom Riders are attacked in the Alabama cities of Anniston and Birmingham
1962	James Meredith breaks the color barrier at the University of Mississippi
1963	Dr. Martin Luther King Jr. delivers his famous "I have a dream" speech at the Lincoln Memorial in Washington, D.C.
1964	Fannie Lou Hamer and others form the Mississippi Freedom Democratic Party in opposition to the state's white-dominated Democratic Party
1964	During "Freedom Summer" in Mississippi, three young civil rights workers are murdered by Klansmen
1964	Congress passes a new civil rights act forbidding discrimination in public places
1965	Dr. Martin Luther King Jr. leads thousands on a march from Selma to Montgomery to demonstrate opposition to the use of literacy tests as a requirement for voting
1965	More than 1,000 people are injured and 200 buildings destroyed in the Watts Riot in Los Angeles, California
1965	Congress passes the Voting Rights Act, outlawing the use of literacy tests
1966	Dr. Ron "Maulana" Karenga creates the African American holiday of Kwanzaa
1967	Thurgood Marshall becomes the first black American to be named to the U.S. Supreme Court
1968	Dr. Martin Luther King Jr. is assassinated in Memphis, Tennessee

Literature List

This is a sampling of recommended books exploring aspects of black history. Check with your librarian for further recommendations including biographies of individual African Americans mentioned in this book and other notable African Americans such as Coretta Scott King, Ida B. Wells, and Jessie Jackson. Look too, for the works of such renowned writers as Christopher Paul Curtis, Virginia Hamilton, Walter Dean Myers, and Patricia and Fred McKissack.

Circle Unbroken

by Margot Theis Raven. Farrar, Straus, and Giroux, 2004. 40 p. Gr. 1–5
A grandmother tells the tale of Gullahs and their beautiful sweetgrass baskets that keep their African heritage alive.

Days of Jubilee: The End of Slavery in the United States

by Pat and Fredrick McKissack. Scholastic, 2003. 144 p. Gr. 4–8
Uses slave narratives, letters, diaries, military orders, and other documents to chronicle the various stages leading to the emancipation of slaves in the United States.

A Dream of Freedom: The Civil Rights Movements from 1954 to 1968

by Diane McWhorter. Scholastic, 2004. 160 p. Gr. 4–8
Pulitzer Prize-winning author Diane McWhorter focuses on the monumental events that occurred between 1954 (the year of Brown v. the Board of Education) and 1968 (the year that Dr. Martin Luther King Jr. was assassinated).

Entrance Place of Wonders: Poems of the Harlem Renaissance

by Daphne Muse. Abrams Books for Young Readers, 2005. 32 p. Gr. 2–6
Twenty poems from the leaders of the Harlem Renaissance including Langston Hughes, James Weldon Johnson, Countee Cullen, and other lesser known poets. Colorful paintings accompany these child-friendly poems suitable for reading aloud.

Free at Last! Stories and Songs of Emancipation

by Doreen Rappaport. Candlewick Press, 2004. 63 p. Gr. 4–8
This companion to the author's No More! Stories and Songs of Slave Resistance draws on first-person accounts in a variety of forms to describe the experiences of African Americans in the South, from the Emancipation in 1863 to the 1954 Supreme Court decision that declared school segregation illegal.

Let It Shine: Stories of Black Women Freedom Fighters

by Angela Davis Pinkney. Gulliver Books, 2000. 120 p. Gr. 4–7
Tells the stories of 10 African American female freedom fighters.

The People Could Fly: The Picture Book

by Virginia Hamilton. Knopf, 2004. 32 p. Gr. 2–8
From Black folklore, a fantasy tale of the slaves who possessed the ancient magic words that enabled them to literally fly away to freedom. Illustrated by Leo and Diane Dillon.

Portraits of African American Heroes

by Tonya Bolded. Dutton Children's Books, 2004. 64 p. Gr. 3–7
A collection of 20 biographical essays about African Americans from Frederick Douglass and W. E. B. Du Bois to Shirley Chisholm and Gwendolyn Brooks.

Remember: The Journey to School Integration

by Toni Morrison. Houghton Mifflin, 2004. 80 p. Gr. 3–8
Unforgettable archival photographs depict the events surrounding school integration.

The Watsons Go to Birmingham

by Christopher Paul Curtis. Delacorte Books for Young Readers, 1995. Gr. 4–8
The ordinary interactions and everyday routines of the Watsons, an African American family living in Flint, Michigan, are drastically changed after they visit Grandma in Alabama in the summer of 1963. Newbery Honor Book.